SIMPLY DREADFUL JOKES

Knock! Knock!
Who's there?
C.
C. Who?
C. me outside!

Knock-knock!
Who's there?
P.!
P. who?
P. King through the keyhole!

Knock-knock!
Who's there?
Annie!
Annie who?
Annie one gonna answer this door?

Knock-knock!
Who's there?
F.!
F. who?
F. you don't hurry up, I'll freeze out here!

Knock-knock!
Who's there?
H.!
H. who?
H. your sandwiches while I was waiting!

Knock-knock!
Who's there?
M.!
M. who?
M. freytfully sorry to disturb you!

Knock-knock!
Who's there?
R.!
R. who?
R. you ever going to answer?

Knock-knock!
Who's there?
N.!
N. who?
N.-chanted to meet you!

Knock-knock!
Who's there?
O.!
O. who?
O.-ping you'll open the door!

Knock-knock!
Who's there?
Z.!
Z. who?
Z. I was coming round, didn't I?

Knock-knock!
Who's there?
Betty
Betty who
Betty lot of people tell you to get
a doorbell!

Knock-knock!
Who's there?
Freezer!
Freezer who?
Freezer jolly good fellow!

Knock-knock!
Who's there?
Adair
Adair who?
Adair when I was young, but now I'm bald!

Knock-knock!
Who's there?
Hippo!
Hippo who?
Hippo-ray! You're in!

Knock-knock!
Who's there?
Doug!
Doug who?
Dougle Blazing - oops - I mean Double Glazing
Salesman!

Knock-knock!
Who's there?
Colin!
Colin who?
Colin round to see if you want to come out!

Knock-knock!
Who's there?
School!
School who?
School out here! Is it warmer inside?

Knock-knock!
Who's there?
Wayne!
Wayne who?
Wayne are you going to open the door?

Knock-knock!
Who's there?
William!
William who?
Williamake an effort and answer the door!

Knock-knock!
Who's there?
Spain!
Spain who?
Spainful knocking on the door for so long!

Knock-knock!
Who's there?
Fred!
Fred who?
Fred I've broken your doorbell!

Knock-knock!
Who's there?
Ivor!
Ivor who?
Ivor good idea what's wrong with your doorbell!

Knock-knock!
Who's there?
Drat!
Drat who?
Drat-a-tat-tat! It makes a change from knock-knock!

Knock-knock!
Who's there?
Joanna!
Joanna who?
Joanna buy a doorbell?

Knock-knock!
Who's there?
Hilda!
Hilda who?
Hilda handle, turn it, and open the door!

Knock-knock!
Who's there?
Walter!
Walter who?
Walter Wall carpeting — bargain prices!

Knock-knock!
Who's there?
Orange!
Orange who?
Orange-ya glad to see me?

Knock-knock!
Who's there?
Herbert!
Herbert who?
Herbert opening the door and letting me in?

Knock-knock!
Who's there?
Cilla!
Cilla who?
Cilla old me! I forgot my key again!

Knock-knock!
Who's there?
I'm a fridge!
I'm a fridge who?
I'm a fridge-yer house is fallin' down!

Knock-knock!
Who's there?
Who!
Who who?
I'm not coming in if there are ghosts in the place!

Knock-knock!
Who's there?
Alaska!
Alaska who?
Alaska man I know to fix your doorbell!

Knock-knock!
Who's there?
Toodle!
Toodle who?
But I've only just got here!

Knock-knock!
Who's there?
Celia!
Celia who?
Celia later! I'm fed up waiting for you to answer the door!

Knock-knock!
Who's there?
Aesop Esau!
Aesop Esau who?
Aesop Esau a puddy tat!

Knock-knock!
Who's there?
Adder!
Adder who?
Adder you get in here?

Knock-knock!
Who's there?
Abba!
Abba who?
Abba banana!

Knock-knock!
Who's there?
Aeron!
Aeron who?
Aeron the side of caution!

Knock-knock!
Who's there?
Humphrey!
Humphrey who?
Humphrey Bonnie Scotland!

Knock-knock!
Who's there?
Len!
Len who?
Len me a raincoat, willya, it's pouring down out here!

Knock-knock!
Who's there?
Agnew!
Agnew who?
Agnew if I just kept on trying, you'd answer the door at last!

Kn-kn!
Kn-kn? Don't you mean 'Knock-knock?'
Not any more, mate! I've broken your knocker!

Knock-knock!
Who's there?
Annie!
Annie who?
Annie more knocking and my hand's going to fall off!

Knock-knock!
Who's there?
Adore!
Adore who?
Adore stands between us — why don't you open it?

Knock-knock!
Who's there?
Justin!
Justin who?
Justin case you didn't know, your doorbell's broken!

Knock-knock!
Who's there?
Agatha!
Agatha who?
Agatha therrible thore thongue, tho I canth thpeak plperly!

Knock-knock!
Who's there?
Bally!
Bally who?
Well, if you're just going to talk nonsense, I might as well go back home!

Knock-knock!
Who's there?
Eammon!
Eammon who?
Eammon a bicycle and ey can't get orff!

Did you hear about the burglar who was caught breaking into a tailor's shop?
He was stitched up good and proper!

Did you hear about the lorry that overturned with a load of margarine?
It was spread all over town!

Did you hear about the new bank in the high street?
They're closing it because of lack of interest!

Did you hear about the man who painted a purple stripe on his hair?
It was headline news!

Did you hear about the man who swam all the way from Dover to Calais?
He didn't believe in ferries!

Did you hear about the electrician who wanted to advertise his business?
He phoned the local radio station and asked for a plug!

Did you hear about the optician who gave up his job?
He didn't see eye-to-eye with his customers!

Did you hear about the werewolf's party last night?
It was a howling success!

Did you hear about the dog with the sore throat?
He was a little husky!

Aeroplane passenger, nervous on first flight —
"Steward, what happens if the plane runs out of fuel?"
Steward — "Then, sir, we all have to get out and push!"

**Steward (to passenger boarding plane with enormous hat
— "Welcome aboard, madame — I see you've brought
your own overhead luggage compartment with you!"**

Traveller (to local, working in his front garden) — "Can
you tell me where this road leads to?"
Local — "Nope!"
Traveller — "In that case, do you know where THAT
road leads to?"
Local — "Nope!"
Traveller — "You don't know much, do you?"
Local — "Nope — but at least I'm not lost!"

Traveller — "I'd like a room for the night please — and
could you make sure that I have a good shower!"
Receptionist — "I think you're old enough to wash
properly by yourself, sir!"

**Station announcement — "Would those taking the
London train please put it back — some people want to
ride on it!"**

Guard — "That's your train over there, sir!"
Traveller — "Cor! I don't get much for my money, do I!"

Traveller — "Is this my train?"
Guard — "No, sir, it's the property of the railway
company!"

Station announcement — "The train standing at platforms 1,2,3 and 4 has just come in sideways!"

What happened when the DJ got a job on the railways? He mixed the tracks!

Traveller — "I love riding the surf!"
Friend — "Does the horse like it too?"

Traveller — "Can I take that train to London?"
Guard — "I suppose you can, sir, but the driver might be a little upset when he comes out and finds it has gone!"

Traveller (to hotel receptionist) — "Do you have a single bedroom with shower?"
Receptionist — "Oh, yes, I do, sir. The staff quarters are excellent here!"

Traveller (phoning airport enquiries) — "How long does it take to get to New York from London?"
Telephonist — "Just a minute, sir. . . "
Traveller — "Thank you very much!"

An elderly lady is sitting on a bus, opposite a boy who is chewing gum.
The old lady looks at the boy, then says — "You can say what you like, young man, but I won't answer — I'm as deaf as a post!"

Traveller — "This room stinks of fish!"
Landlady — "But you said you wanted a sea phew, sir!"

What do you call a man with a rucksack, and salt and pepper all over his head?

A seasoned traveller!

Guard — "Whatever's the matter, sir? You seem terribly angry!"

Traveller — "You bet I'm angry!

I just missed my connection by one minute!"

Guard — "Only one minute, sir? I thought by the fuss you were making you must have missed it by an hour at least!"

Traveller — "How do I get to London in this car?"

Local — "Well, you've got the engine going, so you're off to a good start, sir!"

Traveller — "Do you serve Earl Grey tea in your dining room?"

Hotel Receptionist — "We'll serve anyone tea, provided they're prepared to pay for it, sir!"

Traveller — "Porter! Can I please have a luggage trolley for my wife?"

Porter — "I'm sorry, sir, but wives don't count as luggage!"

Traveller — "How long will the next bus to Glasgow be?"

Local — "Oh, about the same length as the last one, I should think!"

Traveller — "This rail ticket you just sold me is out of date!"

Ticket officer — "That's all right sir; so is the train!"

Airline official — "I'm afraid that your child can't travel on this plane, sir — she hasn't got a ticket!"
Traveller — "But when I booked my ticket, I was told that a little baggage goes free!"

Traveller — "Have you rooms to spare for two tired travellers, footsore and weary?"
Hotel receptionist — "Certainly Mr Footsore. If you and Mr Weary would care to sign the register . . ."

Traveller — "Guard! Why is my train disappearing out of the station? It's five minutes early!"
Railway guard — "Sorry, sir. I think it's my fault. I was just blowing some grit out of my whistle. . ."

Traveller — "I've just returned from Switzerland!"
Friend — "Really? What did you see?"
Traveller — "Not much at all — all these mountains were in the way!"

What's large and grey and wears a flower behind its ear?
A hippy-potamus!

What is the difference between an wolf and a flea?
One howls on the prairie and the other prowls on the hairy!

What did the slug say when it slipped off the wall?
"How slime flies!"

What do worms leave round the bath?
The scum of the earth!

Two flies are sitting on a piece of meat. One fly starts pushing the other.

"Stop!" cries the fly who is being pushed. "You'll put me off my dinner!"

What happened when the cat ate a ball of wool?
She had mittens!

What do you call a dog with a flat nose?
A blunthound!

What kind of dogs do plumbers like?
P(l)ugs!

What kind of dogs do mountaineers like?
Pekes!

What kind of dogs do landladies like?
Boarder collies!

What did the trumpet player call his dog?
Blew!

What kind of dogs do mechanics like?
Spannerels!

What kind of dogs do scientists like best?
Lab-radors!

What kind of dog lives on cream?
The whippet!

What kind of dog did the robber have?
A Doberman pincher!

Did you hear about the film about lots of dogs with no spots?
They called it 101 Dullmations!

What kind of dog do sprinters like best?
The daschund!

Why was the dog crying?
Because it was a tear-rier!

Why was the other dog crying?
Because it was a chi-wah-wah!

What kind of dog does a pessimist have?
A disa-pointer!

What did the cleaner call his dog?
Dusty!

What did the electrician call his dog?
Sparky!

What did the dentist call his dog?
Floss!

What did the demolition man call his dog?
Rex!

What did the doctor call his dog?
Spot!

What did the gardener call his dog?
Bud!

What did the car mechanic call his dog?
Rusty!

What did the yachtsman call his dog?
Bob!
What did the musician call his dog?
Hi-doh!

What did the wine merchant call his dog?
Corky!

What did the boatman call his dog?
Row-ver!

What kind of dogs do they keep in monasteries?
Monkrels!

What did the optician call his dog?
Glassie!

What kind of dog do crossword compilers like best?
The setter!

What did the road mender call his dog?
Digger!

What did the photographer call his dog?
Flash!

What did the cricketer call his dog?
Stumpy!

What did the baker call his dog?
The baker didn't have a dog — he had a bunny!

What kind of dog do cattle farmers like best?
Bull terriers!

What kind of dogs always live on farms?
St Barnyards!

What kind of dogs do gymnasts like best?
Springer spaniels!

What kind of dogs do teachers like best?
Ssh-now!-zers!

What did the fireman do with his cat?
He put it out at night!

What do you do with a ghost dog?
Exorcise it daily!

What did the dog say when it sat on some sandpaper?
"Ruff, ruff!"

Two fleas are sitting by the roadside when a man
comes along with five dogs on leads. One flea sighs,
and says to his friend —
"Wouldn't you know it, you wait all day for one of these
things and then several come along at once!"

What happened when the dog swallowed a tropical fish?
It had guppies!

Where did the banker get his dog?
From the pound!

What do you give a dog with a cold?
A chew!

What kind of dogs do skinflints like best?
Cheapdogs!

What kind of dogs do electricians like best?
Wire-haired terriers!

What kind of dogs do office managers like best?
Chairman shepherds!

When is a dog like an archeologist?
When it digs up old bones!

When is a dog like a piano player?
When he gives you a good chewin'!

How do you clean up after a ghost dog?
Use a whoo-oo-per scooper!

When is a detective like a dog?
When he's on a lead!

How does a dog ask for a share in its owner's ice cream?
It says "Arf! arf!"

Bill — "My dog's a sniffer dog!"
Will — "Well, train it to use a handkerchief!"

Where does the squirrel keep his dog?
In a kernel out the back!

Did you hear about the problem they had with the computers at the police station?
The sergeant couldn't get the PC's to work!

Traveller — "What's holding the trains up today, guard?"
Guard — "Wheels and axles, same as any other day, sir!"

Traveller — "How far is it to the next village, as the crow flies?"
Local — "Oh, about 1076 flaps, sir!"

Traveller — "Do you know the way to the railway station?"
Local — "Oh, yes, thank you. I'll manage to find it myself!"

Traveller — "Do you serve breakfast in this hotel?"
Hotel Receptionist — "Oh, no, sir. The waiters do that!"

Traveller — "Guard! Where is this train going to?"
Guard — "This train is going to London in twenty minutes, sir!"
Traveller — "Gosh, that's quick — last time I went to London by train it took three hours!"

1st Traveller — "I've been in Paris three days now, and I haven't been to the Louvre yet!"
2nd Traveller — "You should eat more fruit!"

Two aliens, landing in Great Britain for the first time, walked up to a post box and asked it the way to London. Naturally, it did not reply.
"Don't just stand there grinning," said the first alien to the post box. "Can't you see we're lost?"

Aeroplane passenger on trans-Atlantic flight — "How far are we from land?"
Steward — "Only about a mile!"
Passenger — "As the crow flies?"
Steward — "No, as a stone falls!"

Traveller — "Do you know how to get to King's Cross?"
Little boy — "Steal their crowns?"

A traveller arrived at a small country railway station. There was no-one around, and the first thing he noticed was a sign on a door "Ladies Not Working".
He turned the corner and found another sign "Gents Out of Action".
Furious, he found a telephone box and called the director of the railway company. "Tell me," he said, "if the ladies aren't working and the gents are out of action, who do you think is going to drive the train?"

Traveller — "Does this bus stop at the pier?"
Driver — "If it doesn't, swim for your life!"

Tourist (as his car screeches to a halt at the roadside) — "Quick! Can you tell me the way to Robert Burns' cottage?"
Local — "No need to hurry — you've missed him by a couple of hundred years!"

Traveller (to elderly local) — "And have you lived here all your life?"
Local — "Not yet!"

What did the greedy man say to his dog?
Wolf down!

What did the dog say when it saw the firework go off?
"WOOF!"

Fred — "I think my dog's a gun-dog!"
Ted — "What do you mean by that?"
Fred — "Every time I call him, he shoots off!"

What's bouncy and playful and wears a dog collar?
A puppy, of course!
Anything else?
The minister on his day off!

Why did the butcher put ten canaries in the mincer?
To make cheep sausage meat!

What's black and white and goes round and round?
A rolled-up newspaper!

What else is black and white and goes round and round?
A zebra in a revolving door!

What else is black and white and goes round and round?
A zebra in a cement mixer!

What else is black and white and goes round and round?
A zebra on the waltzers!

Maisie — "My poodle cost £500!"
Mo — "I wouldn't call that a poodle —
I'd call it a dearhound!"

Why do dogs smell?
Because they never change their coats!

Have you ever wondered why zebras do so many silly things?
Yes — I asked them, but I didn't get an answer!
Why?
Zebras can't talk!

Daddy Bear — "Who's been eating my porridge?"
Baby Bear — "Who's been eating my porridge?"
Mummy Bear — "Calm down! I haven't made it yet!"

"I'm calling my dog Carpenter!"
"Why?"
"Because he does odd jobs around the house!"

Jimmy — "I got a goldfish for my birthday!"
Joe — "That's nice!"
Jimmy — "Yes — it's a pity I have to wait till next birthday for the bowl!"

What do you get if you cross a model with a cat?
A glamour puss!

Baby Bear — "Who's been eating my porridge?"
Daddy Bear — "Burp!"

What do you call a v in a playground?
Ee-aw, Marjorie Daw!

Did you hear the joke about the slippery eel?
You wouldn't grasp it!

Did you hear the story about the peacock?
It's a wonderful tale!

What creature can see just as well from either end?
A hippopotamus with its eyes shut!

The lion is walking through the jungle, asking every animal
he meets, "Who is king of the jungle?"
He asks the monkey, he asks the crocodile, he asks the parrot,
"Who is king of the jungle?" and without exception, they all
give the same answer; "You, your majesty, you are king of
the jungle!"
Then he comes to the elephant. "Who is king of the jungle?"
he asks the elephant. The elephant says nothing, but picks the
lion up with his trunk and flings him against a nearby tree.
The lion winces with pain.
"All right," he says to the elephant. "So you don't know the
answer — but did you have to get so cross about it?"

What happens when the cows get mixed up at the
dairy?
Udder chaos!

How do you get a set of teeth put in for free?
Annoy a guard dog!

What kind of poultry do you get in sport?
Ducks in cricket and fowls in football — and there's always some old grouse among the spectators!

Why were no frogs born in 2001?
Because it wasn't a Leap Year!

Why did the pigeon go to the race track?
For a flutter on the horses!

Why did the whale let Jonah go?
He couldn't stomach him!

Why can the leopard never escape from the zoo?
Because he's always spotted!

How do you stop a dog from barking in the back of the car?
Put it in the front!

What did one racehorse say to the other?
"Your pace is familiar — have we met before?"

Two ants are running along the top of a packet of biscuits. one says to the other, "What's the rush?" The other replies, "Can't you read? It says 'Tear along the dotted line'!"

What did one sardine say to the other sardine when they saw a submarine?
"Fancy opening a can of people?"

How did the chihuahua kill the alsatian?
It got stuck in its throat and choked it!

What do you get if you cross a rabbit with a shallot?
Bunions!

What's small, black, and stars in Kung Fu movies?
Bruce Flea!

Why are goldfish like cartoon characters?
Because they speak in bubbles!

Why did the horse go to school?
He wanted hay-grades!

Where do squid go camping?
In their tentacles!

What's got six eyes but can't see?
Three blind mice!

Why did the chicken go fishing?
She wanted a perch for dinner!
What did the parrot say to the float?
"Who's a pretty buoy, then?"!

What did the mother kangaroo say when her baby was
snatched from her pouch?
"Stop! Pickpocket!"

Why did the rabbit go to the beauty parlour?"
Because it was having a bad hare day!

How can you move a really heavy pig?
With a pork-lift truck!

What do you call a thieving rooster?
A cock robbin'!

Why did the scientists refuse to clone the parrot?
Because it repeated itself already!

What's large and hairy and can break the sound barrier?
King Kongcorde!

Where do limpets go camping?
They don't have tentacles, so they sleep in barnacles!

How did the chicken pay for her
groceries?
She put them on her egg-spense account!

Did you hear about the sheep's choir?
They all sang in ewe-nison!

Never eat in a bull's restaurant.
  — They charge for seconds!

Newsflash — "Disaster in the jungle. Elephants are
sending a special tuskforce to deal with it."

Did you hear about the absent-minded chicken?
She mislaid her eggs!

Did you hear about the pigeon who wanted to buy New York?
He put a deposit on the Statue of Liberty!

1st fly — "I hear poor Freddy was squashed inside an atlas!"
2nd fly — "Yes — but he always wanted to put himself on the map!"

Maisie — "My new puppy has a pedigree!"
Mo — "Do you have papers for it?"
Maisie — "Not any more — it's house-trained now!"
What do you call a line of cats?
A purrade!

How do you get your dishes squeaky clean?
Put a mouse in your dishwasher!

What do camels take in their tea?
One hump or two!

What did the skunk take to read on holiday?
A best-smeller!

Why did the bear drive round in circles?
Every time he came to a junction, he saw a sign saying
'Bear Left'!

How do you teach a duck new words?
Buy it a duck-tionary!

How fast can a duck go?
At a quacking pace!

Why do people throw bits of bread to the ducks?
Because they've eaten all the cakes!

What did the duck say when she bought a tube of lipstick at
the drugstore?
"Just put that on my bill, will you?"

Why did the chicken cross the road?
For a joke!

Why did the breadcrumbs cross the road?
They were stuck to the chicken legs!

Why did the musician cross the road?
For a new set of drumsticks!

Why did the crow get an enormous telephone bill?
He made too many caw-lls!

Why did the jackdaw cross the road?
To crow about his success!

Why did the dalmation disappear?
His owner used spot remover!

Why did the farmer cross the road?
To find his wandering poultry!
How can you tell if a chicken likes you?
It gives you a peck on the cheek!

Man in pet-shop — "You've got a talking dog advertised for sale. Can I hear it speak?"
Pet-shop owner — "Sure! Come here, Barney, and tell the man something about yourself!"
Dog — "Hi! I'm Barney! I'm a world-champion long-distance runner, and I've climbed Everest three times!"
Customer — "That's incredible! (To pet-shop owner) Why would you want to part with such an incredible dog?"
Pet-shop owner — "I'm sick of his lies!"

How did the baby chicken manage to cross the road safely?
Beginner's cluck!

What do you get if you cross a dog with a cheetah?
A dog that chases cars-then overtakes them!

Why should you never trust a nanny-goat?
Because she might be kidding!

Why did the duck cross the road?
To prove he wasn't chicken!

What happened to the chicken who was left out of the henhouse in winter?
He became a brr-rd!

Why did the bird fall out of the sky?
It was dead, silly!

What do you call a canary on roller blades?
A cheepskate!

Bertie Bear calls round at Willy Wolf's house. He rings the bell, but gets no answer. So he checks his watch and says, "What's the time? Missed the wolf!"

What do you get if you cross a dog with a giraffe?
An animal that barks at low-flying aircraft!

Why do bears wear fur coats?
Because their raincoats are at the cleaners!

Teacher — "The pheasant is a game
bird . . ."
Pupil — "What game does it like best?"

What do crabs do when they run out of food?
They nip down to the shops for some more!

What did the frog say on the golf course?
Divot!

Golfer — "Where's my golf ball, Fido?"
Dog — "Rough! Rough!"

1st fly — "I hurt my feet tap-dancing!"
2nd fly — "How did you manage that?"
1st fly — "I burnt them — it was the hot tap!"

Farmer — "Sorry sir, we have no eggs — the batteries have
run down!"

Who won the obstacle race in the jungle?
The cheetah was first over the lion!

Why did the bear get his head shaved?
Because he wanted a de-fur-ent hairstyle!

What do you call a male parrot?
Polly-fella!

Why can chickens never tell their children apart?
Because they all look eggsactly the same!

What did the maths teacher say when his parrot went missing?
"Polygon!"

What did the snake do when he had a headache?
He took some asp-irin!

Why did the chicken go to the theatre?
To see its favourite comedy-hen!

What did the sow give her husband for his birthday?
A pig's tie!

Where does the captain exercise his dog on board ship?
The poop deck!

1st rabbit — "I've got an idea!"
2nd rabbit — "Not another of your hair-brained schemes!"

Did you hear about the worm that lived to be 100?
He always got up before the early bird!

What's a flea's favourite song?
"Home on the mange!"

Why did the zoo-keeper end up in hospital?
The boa constrictor had a crush on him!

Mum — "Where on earth did you get that elephant, Johnny?"
Johnny — "At the Jumbo Sale!"

Why was the buffalo smiling?
Because it was laugh-a-bull!

Why did the hare's friend's think he was boring?
He just kept rabbiting on an on . . .

What do you call a pigeon in uniform?
A military coo!

How do hens dance?
Chick-to-chick!

Why did the chickens leave the dance floor?
Because they heard the foxtrot!

What ballet do pigs most enjoy?
Swine Lake!

Why did the cow cough?
It had a bullfrog in its throat!

Which animal goes to bed with its shoes on?
The horse!

Why did the sheep fail its driving test?
Because it couldn't do a ewe-turn!

Why are mosquitoes good at arithmetic?
Because they add to your misery and subtract from your pleasure!

Why are rabbits good at arithmetic?
Because they multiply faster than most other animals!

What's the easiest way to count cattle?
With a cow-culator!

What do you call a shrimp with a machine gun?
Al Caprawn!

What happens when chickens drink whisky?
They lay Scotch eggs!

Why did the cows all sit down at once?
They were playing moo-sical bumps!

What is the difference between a diving duck and a lost dog?
A diving duck up-ends in the pond, and a lost dog ends up in the pound!

What did the chicken say when its mother sat on an orange?
"Look at the egg mamma-laid!"

What do you get if you cross a dog with a chicken?
Pooched eggs!

What do you give a horse with a chest infection?
Cough stirrup!

Why did the cat wear a turtle-neck sweater?
To hide his flea-collar!

How do dogs cook their eggs?
They pooch them!

Why did Mr and Mrs Skunk sit at opposite sides of the church?
They refused to share the same pew!

What do you call an ant which has come from abroad?
Important!

What do you call an ant with a high voice?
Descant!

Why do cats make bad sailors!
Every time they set sail, there's a mew-tiny!

What do you call an ant that has fallen in the paint pot?
A colourant!

What happens when a firefly becomes confused?
It doesn't know if it's coming or glowing!

What do you call a sweetly smelling ant?
Fragrant!

What do you call a helpful ant?
Assistant!

What do you get when you send two rockets full of toads into
space?
Star Warts!

Why do frogs have webbed feet?
To stamp out forest fires!

Why do elephants have singed feet?
From stamping on smoking frogs!

Why do frogs wear tin helmets?
To protect them from stamping elephants!

Why did the frog break off his engagement?
His girlfriend spawned his affections!

What's green, covered in ketchup and mustard, and rolls?
Hot frogs!

What happens if you eat a poisoned frog?
You croak!

Why did the frog go to the doctor?
He had a troublesome person in his throat!

Two cats had a milk-drinking race
The first one won by a lap!

What do you call an ant that can swim?
An ant-phibian!

What did one vulture say to the other vulture?
"I've got a bone to pick with you!"

How do American cats get around town?
In catillacs!

1st maggot — "What's the matter?"
2nd maggot — "I'm in despair!"
1st maggot — "Well try dis apple instead, it might cheer you up!"

Why did the horse go to the theatre?
It wanted a stall for Saturday night!

When is it unlucky to see a black cat?
When you're a mouse!

What lies on the ground, 100 feet up in the air, and smells?
A dead centipede!
Mummy centipede — "What's the matter, son?"
Little centipede — "I've hurt my foot!"
Mummy centipede — "Which one?"
Little centipede — "Hang on — I'm still counting!"

What's speckled and travels at 100 miles an hour?
A trout on a motor bike!

How do you get milk from a cat?
Steal her saucer!

What do you do if you find a bookworm eating your book?
Take the words right out of its mouth!

Why did the cat cry over her maths homework?
Because the sums were im-puss-able!

What do you do with a hyperactive dog?
Press paws!

What did one flea say to the other flea after a night out?
"Shall we walk home or catch a dog?"

What did Wild Bill Hickock call his cat?
Posse!

1st golfer — "What's that little grey creature holding up your golf ball?"
2nd golfer — "That's my-tee mouse!

What do you do with a dog that chases everything on a bike?
Take the air out of its tyres!

1st man — "My dog loves children!"
2nd man — "Does he?"
1st man — "Yes, but he has to make do with dog meat instead!"

Did you hear about the cat that kept thinking it was Mickey Mouse?
It was having Disney spells!

What do you call a rich frog?
A gold-blooded reptile!

What do you do if a frog turns up at your party uninvited?
Tell him to hop it!

What do you call a frog spy?
A croak-and-dagger agent!

Do mice give each other Christmas presents?
No — they just exchange Chris-mouse cards!

What do you call a homeless snail?
A slug!

How do sheep record special family events?
They make videos with their lambcorder!

What do you call a nervous flea?
A jitterbug!

When is an amphibian like a car?
When it's being toad!

What do you call a hen that is covered in oil?
A slick chick!

What happened to the wolf who swallowed a sheep whole?
He felt very baa-aa-aa-d!

Why did the sheep choose the most expensive washing machine?
Because it was easiest to ewes!

What kind of birds are found in Portugal?
Portu-geese!

Bill — "My dog can count!"
Will — "Prove it!"
Bill — "Okay! Rover, what is four minus four?"
Will — "But he's saying nothing!"
Bill — "Exactly! That's the right answer!"

What did the dog say to the bone?
"It's been nice gnawing you!"

Did you hear the joke about the egg?
Never mind — it was rotten anyway!

Café owner to little boy — "You can't bring your dog in here — it's smelly and full of germs!"
Little boy — "If it's as bad as that, then I don't want to come in, either!"

What's the difference between lions and whales when they're upset?
Lions roar, but whales blubber!

Why do birds go to the library?
To look for bookworms!

What do you get if you put a skunk in Concorde?
A plane that stinks to high heaven!

Teacher — "Name six things that contain wheat."
Pupil — "Bread, cakes and four fields."

When is an eagle faster than a jumbo jet?
When it's taking a ride in Concorde!

Bertie — "Can my dog be buried in the pet's cemetery?"
Dad; — "No!"
Bertie — "Why?"
Dad — "Because he's not dead!"

What do you get from criminal cows?
Bad milk!

Fred — "Have you ever seen a horsefly?"
Ted — "No, but I have seen a sheep dip!"

Can skunks sing?
No, but they don't half hum!

What is the strongest of all birds?
The Crane!

What's warm and smelly and goes round and round?
A skunk in the tumble drier!

What fur do we get from a grizzly bear?
As fur away as possible!

Why did the antelope?
Nobody gnu!

What flies round the light at night, biting other insects' heads off?
The tiger moth!

How do baby lions cross the road safely?
They wait until they see a zebra crossing!

What's stripey and goes up and down?
A tiger on a pogo stick!

Why did the desert animals get not Christmas presents last year?
Because the lion had sandy claws!

How do you know that carrots are good for the eyes?
Because you never see a rabbit wearing spectacles!

Why is a lame dog like adding 6 and 7?
Because he puts down three and carries one!

What is worse than a giraffe with sore throat?
A centipede with chilblains!,

What has one hundred feet and sings in a high voice?
A soprano centipede!

How do you keep flies out of your kitchen?
Put a pile of rotting food in your living room!

What games do ants play with elephants?
Squash!

Why are there no penguins in the Sahara?
Because their chocolate would melt in the sun!

What do you call an ant who always wants do things
by himself?
Independ-ant!

What do you call an ant with five pairs of eyes?
Ant-ten-eye!

What do cows like best from the Chinese takeaway?
Moo-dles!

What did the dog say when it finally caught its tail?
"This is the giddy limit!"

What do cat actors say on stage?
"Tabby or not tabby!"

What's black, yellow and covered in blackberries?
A bramble bee!

What has fifty legs but can't walk?
Half a centipede!

Why did the centipede miss his train?
He had to stop to tie his bootlaces!

What do you call a centipede on guard duty?
A sentrypede!

What goes ninety nine, clickety, ninety nine, clickety splosh?
A centipede in River Dance!

Why are cats the funniest animals?
Because they are most a-mews-ing!

What does a queen bee do when she burps?
She issues a royal pardon!

What do you call an ant who cannot sing in tune?
Discord-ant!

What do you call a maggot who becomes an ace pilot?
Buggles!

Why did the ladybird go to the doctor?
Because she had spots!

What kind of medicine do you give a sick ant?
Ant-ibiotics!

What do baby mice look like after their baths?
Squeaky clean!

Where do flies meet before they go into town?
At the buzz stop!

What has six legs, and can work out your dad's income tax?
An account-ant!

Where do caterpillars lay their heads at night?
On their caterpillows!

Why did Mr and Mrs Spider keep a money box under their mattress?
They were saving for their golden webbing!

Why did the hedgehog cross the road?
To see his flat mate!

What would you get if you gave lemon juice to a cat?
A sour puss!

Why do elephants wear green shoes?
So they can hide in the grass!

What kind of bears like rainy weather?
Drizzly bears!

What kind of maths do owls like best?
Owlgebra!

What do you call a camel with three humps?
Humphrey!

How do you stop two snakes from having an argument?
Tell them to hiss and make up!

What do you say to a bald porcupine?
Anything you like — he's too spineless to do anything about it!

Did you hear about the tiger who swallowed a comedian?
He felt very funny!

What did the man-eating tiger cook for lunch?
Baked beings!

What do you call a woodpecker with no beak?
A headbanger!

How does a bird with a broken wing manage to land safely?
With its sparrowchute!

Why was the snake kept in at school?
Because his writhing was bad!

What did one firefly say to the other?
Got to glow now!

Where do spiders play football?
Webley!

What did the spider say when it got a hole in its web?
"Darn it!"

Why should you never go to a shop owned by elephants?
Because they charge too much!

Why was the chicken sent off the football pitch?
Because it was a fowl!

Why are spiders computer wizards?
Check out their websites for more information!

What is black and white and red all over?
A zebra with an allergy!

1st glow worm — "I'm delighted!"
2nd glow worm — "But you look miserable!"
1st glow worm — "I am. Someone cut off my tail and I'm de-lighted!"

What do you get if you cross a skunk with a bat?
A smell that hangs around all day!

What did the mouse say when he was leaving his friend's house?
See you next squeak!

Why did the rhinoceros buy a bicycle bell?
Because his horn wasn't working!

Why did the chicken cross the adventure playground?
To get to the other slide!

What is black and white and green, black and white and green?
A zebra wrestling with a gooseberry!

Why was Charlie glow worm always top of the class?
Because he was the brightest!

How did the owls get into Noah's Ark?
Two-hoo by two-hoo!

What happens when flies become cold?
They turn into bluebottles!

Why did the two maggots in an apple get turned away
from Noah's Ark?
Because the animals were supposed to be in pairs!

Why did the lame chicken go to the music shop?
To get another drumstick!

How do you find where a flea has bitten you?
Start from scratch!

What do you call a Russian flea?
A Moscow-ito!

What do you get if you cross a skunk with a boomerang?
A bad smell that keeps coming back.

What is worse than finding a maggot when you bite into an apple?
Finding half a maggot!

Which side of a hen has the most feathers?
The outside!

If there were six cats in a boat and one jumped out, how many would be left?
None! All the rest were copy cats!

What do you get if you cross a young goat with a maggot?
A grubby kid!

What do sea monsters eat?
Fish and ships!

1st cat — "I'm feeling down in the mouth!"
2nd cat — "Why is that?"
1st cat — "I caught a duck earlier on today!"

What is a French cat's favourite pudding?
Chocolate mousse!

A dog in a cowboy hat, with a bandage on his foot, limped into a Wild West Saloon. "What are you doin' here, stranger?" asked the barman. The dog growled and replied, "I'm lookin' for the man who shot ma paw!"

Why was the centipede late?
Because he was playing "This little piggy" with his baby sister.

What do you get if you cross a centipede with a minah bird?
A walkie-talkie!

What do you get if you cross a centipede with a chicken?
Enough drumsticks to feed an army!

What is worse than a crocodile with toothache?
A centipede with athlete's foot!

What do you get if you cross a dog with a gorilla?
An animal that won't let you up on the couch!

What did Mr Dopey do to the flea in his ear?
He shot it!

What do you get if you cross a glow-worm with a glass of beer?
Light ale!

How do you know when a spider's angry?
He goes up the wall!

What goes "snap, crackle, pop"?
A firefly with a short circuit!

What is the name of the most famous insect movie producer?
Stephen Spielbug!

A man goes into the riding supplies shop and asks the first man he sees for a new bridle for his horse. "I'm sorry, but I can't help you, sir," says the man. "I'm a saddle sewer." "Look here," says the first man, "I've been riding for three days to get here, and I'm pretty saddle sore myself, but do you hear me moaning about it?"

What do you get if you cross a bee with a skunk?
A bee with a nasty stink in its tail!

What kind of dog makes a good hairdresser?
A shampoodle!

What is a vampire's favourite kind of dog?
A bloodhound!

How do you catch a runaway dog?
Hide behind a tree and make a noise like a bone!

What do you call a happy sheepdog?
A jolly collie!

What did the cowboy say when a bear ate his dog?
"Well, doggone!"

What kind of dog loves the smell of flowers?
A budhound!

What do you get if you cross a sheepdog with a daisy?
A collie-flower!

Why did the poor dog chase its tail?
He was trying to make both ends meet!

Bob — "Why did you call your dog 'Discovery'?"
Joe — "Because I've never seen anything like him before!"

Annie — "Why did you call your dog 'germ'?"
Betty — "Because I got him from a friend!"

Where does a Rottweiler sit in the cinema?
Anywhere it wants to!

What kind of meat do you give a stupid dog?
Chump chops!

Why did the dachshund bite the woman's ankle?
Because that was the only part of her he could reach!

Bill — "Why do you call your dog Frost?"
Will — "Because Frost bites!"

Why do dogs wag their tails?
Because no-one else will do it for them!

Bill — "Have you heard about the dog that ate twelve cloves of garlic?"
Will — "No — what about him?"
Bill — "His bark was much worse than his bite!"

What do you call a meditating dog?
A paws for thought!

Why do dogs bury their bones in the earth?
Because they can't dig a hole in the pavement!

Bill — "My dog's so clever, he can answer the telephone!"
Will — "What kind of dog is he?"
Bill — "A golden receiver!"

What do you get if you cross an aeroplane and a dog?
A jet setter!

What can you do if your dog eats your shoes?
Wear your boots instead!
What's the difference between a bear and a hot dog?
A bear wears a fur coat, a hot dog just pants!

What do you get if you cross a teddy bear with a skunk?
Winnie the Poo-ee!

How can you tell if it's been raining cats and dogs?
There are poodles on the streets!

What is the name of the bear who wears wellington
boots and steps in puddles?
Paddlington!

Why are bears bad at dancing?
They have two left feet!

What do you get if you cross a skunk with a faithful dog?
A bad smell that follows you around!

What do you get if you cross a kangaroo with a dog?
A pooch with a pouch!

How can you find a dog in the woods?
Put your ear to a tree a listen for its bark!

What is grey, has big ears and a trunk?
A mouse going on holidays!

What sport do flies play with humans?
Squash!

1st furniture polisher — "So you're pleased with your
new puppy, then?
2nd furniture polisher — "Oh, yes, I've taken quite a
shine to him!"

1st weather forecaster — "What's your new baby like?"
2nd weather forecaster — "Oh, you know the sort of
thing fair, windy, occasionally wet!"

Friend — "Why did you give up your job as a
fishmonger?"
Fishmonger — "It was making me sell-fish!"

What kind of football do bankers play?
Fiver side!

What's a hairdresser's favourite sport?
Curling!

Did you hear about the butcher who joined the union?
He wanted to become chop steward!

Salesman — "So you want a career in sales, do you — do you ever tell lies?"
Job applicant — "No, but I'll learn quickly!"

Why did the baker stop making doughnuts?
because he was tired of the hole business!

Why did the traffic cop arrest the sheep?
Because it did a ewe-turn on a dual carriageway!

Why did the banker fall off his bike?
He lost his balance!

Did you hear about the footballer who became a pilot?
He was sacked for playing on the wing!

Why did the farmer feed his cows five-pound notes?
To make the milk richer!

Why did the farmer build the cattle-shed squint?
To get lean beef!

Why did the farmer daub stripes on his pigs?
To get streaky bacon!

1st fisherman — "I caught five mackerel yesterday, all
of them weighing more than three pounds!"
2nd fisherman — "So what? I caught six jellyfish — all
of them different flavours!"

What team do car mechanics support?
The Oil Stars!

Why did the chef get a job in a roof-top restaurant?
He wanted to be a high-fryer!

Did you hear about the lift attendant who got a job as
an airline steward?

As the passengers boarded the plane, he asked them, "Going up?"

What did the movie star call out to his adoring fans?
"See you swoon!"

What is the difference between a night watchman and a butcher?
One stays awake and the other weighs a steak!

Why do inventors make useless cooks?
Because most of their ideas are half-baked!

Did you hear about the submarine captain who got a job driving a subway train?

Every time he stopped at a station, he shouted "Up periscope!"

Why did they call in the glazier to the atomic power plant?
They wanted new clear (nuclear) windows!

What part of the police force can bacon join?
The Special Brunch!

Why was the writer kept in prison?
He hadn't finished his sentence!

Why did the lawyer go to the skating-rink?
Too see just-ice!

Did you hear about the chef that burnt through all his saucepans?
The manager told him he would make a good potholer!

Take up astronomy — it's a heavenly job!

Take up astrology — there's a future in it!

Take up aromatherapy — you'll soon get the massage!

Take up a litter collection — you'll pick it up as you go along!

Work in a casino — spin the roulette wheel and watch things take a turn for the better!

WHAT DO YOU
CALL A NERVOUS
WITCH?

A TWITCH!

What do they sing when someone retires from the frozen foods factory?
"Freezer jolly good fellow!"

What did the supermarket manager say to the late employee?
There's trouble in store for you!

Why was the weatherman depressed?
Because there were too many clouds on his horizon!
What's the difference between a baker and a cricketer?
One makes buns and rolls and the other makes runs and bowls!

What did the weatherman say when he had beans for supper?
"Gale force wind predicted later on tonight!"

What did the miserly weatherman write on his bathroom door?
"Brief showers only!"

Musician — "Do you know 'Madame Butterfly'?"
Man — "Know her? She's been my friend since she was a cocoon!"

1st archeologist — "I'm sorry we quarrelled. Can we be friends again, and forget about our little argument?
2nd archeologist — "Certainly. I've always said there's nothing to be gained from digging up the past."

Did you hear about the card-player who bought a double-decker bus?
He tried to drive under a low bridge, and cut the top deck!

Man (to barber) — "Would you shave a man with a wooden leg?"
Barber — "No — with a razor!"

Optometrist — "How many fingers am I holding up Mr Smith?"
Mr Smith — "Goodness — you're even more short-sighted than I am!"

1st Farmer — "I haven't had enough rain for my crops this year!"
2nd farmer — "You've had more than I have!"
1st farmer — "How can that be?"
2nd farmer — "You've got more land!"

Tex jumped onto his saddle and galloped out of town into the desert in a cloud of dust. Two minutes later, he was back. He had forgotten his horse!

What did the banker say when the butcher's safe blew up?
"It wasn't my vault!"

Friend — "So you've given up your job as host on the TV show, have you?"
TV personality — "Yes — I came, I saw, I compered!"

What was written on the magician's gravestone?
"I came, I sawed, I conjured!"

Man — "I make a lot of money in my new job!"
Friend — "What's that?"
Man — "I work at the mint!"

ESKIMO   ESKIMOO

IGLOO   EGGLOO

A farmer is standing in a field with forty pigs — how many feet are there?
Two — the pigs have trotters!

What did the electrician say to his teenage son?
"Wire you insulate?"!

Why is a telephone engineer like an explorer?
Because his work takes him from pole to pole!

Window cleaner — "I fell off a fifty-foot ladder yesterday!"
Friend — "Did you hurt yourself?"
Window cleaner — "No — I was only on the second rung!"

Did you hear about the comedian who took up chicken farming?
The chickens got plenty of corn!
What about the eggs?
Oh — they kept cracking up!

Ted — "I started at the bottom in my career!"
Fred — "Did you?"
Ted — "Yes — I got a job in a toilet paper factory!"

How did the beautician remember her clients' names?
She kept them all on file!

Why was the sword-swallower arrested?
Because he hiccuped and stabbed a member of the audience!

What is the difference between a film star and an enormous sweater?
One's a crowd-drawer, the other's a drawer-crowder!

"Did it hurt when you fell of the piano stool?"
"No — I hit the soft pedal!"

Why did the little boy trip up the waiter?
He wanted to see a flying saucer!

When is a bus-driver not a bus-driver?
When he turns into a side-street!

Why was the shoemaker relieved?
Because he had found his hammer at last!

Did you hear about the man whose wife bought a whisky
firm?
He loved her still!

They stopped using string at the packaging plant. It was tape for the parcels or nothing. Every day, bits of string would queue up at the door, looking for a job, only to be turned away. Then one day, a tassel turned up at the door. The man at the door looked at him and said, "Are you a bit of string?" "No," said the tassel. "I'm a frayed knot."

Why did the nurse put a band-aid on her pay check?
Because she got a cut in her salary!

Why did the person with second-sight get depressed?
Because nothing surprised him any more!

What is the difference between a dentist and an artist?
One draws teeth, the other just draws!

Why did the barber go to the bank?
To open a shaving account!

Why did the public speaker go to the bank?
To open a say-things account!

Why did the duck farmer go out of business?
Because profits were down!

Why was the prize-fighter house-proud?
Because he wiped the floor with his opponent!

At the grand parade this afternoon, most of the crowd were waving flags.
The hairdresser didn't have a flag, so she waved her hair instead!

The edition published 2008 by
Geddes & Grosset,
David Dale House,
New Lanark, ML11 9DJ, Scotland

© 2008 Geddes & Grosset

ISBN 978 1 84205 675 2

Printed and bound in the UK